£7.99

Welcome

This annual belongs to:

MINI MYSTERY ??

There are **10** hidden fingerprints in this Annual that could be vital clues. Help the gang find them and list the page numbers below!

Answers on page 61.

Contents

THIS OLD HAUNTED HOUSE

SHOLLY FISCH
STORY

SCOTT JERALDS
PENCILS

JEFF ALBRECHT
INKS

HEROIC AGE
COLORS

MIKE SELLERS
LETTERS

MICHAEL SIGLAIN AND
JEANINE SCHAEFER
EDITORS

CONTINUED ON PAGE 12

9

Best Foot Forward!

Now this is the way to keep your pens and pencils tidy on your desk! This Bigfoot pencil holder is totally awesome!

YOU WILL NEED:

scissors, a cardboard tube, thick card, kitchen paper, PVA glue, sticky tape, newspaper, paints and a paintbrush, brown fun fur.

Like, Bigfoot is one big hairy dude! He stands about 7 feet tall and has a big cone-shaped head. Also known as Sasquatch, this furry fella lives in the isolated woods of North America. Spooky-Doo!

1

Draw and cut out a large foot shape from card. Tape the cardboard tube to the back of the foot. This will be the ankle which forms the pencil storage section.

2 Roll up five balls of newspaper as toes and tape them into place. Pad out the rest of the foot with scrunched up newspaper.

3 Cover the whole foot in two layers of paper mache and leave it to dry.

4 Paint the toes pale pink with black details. Paint the inside of the cardboard tube black.

Ask an adult to help

5 Cover the rest of the foot in brown fur. The easiest way to do this is to cut a hole in a large piece of fur, big enough for the cardboard tube to go through. Cover the foot with glue and place the fur over the tube. Glue down the fur and trim the edges around the base of the foot and around the toes. Wrap a piece of fur around the ankle.

GLUE

CONTINUED ON PAGE 28

24

MYSTERY MONSTER!

Can you work out which mythical monster is hiding within these lines?
Colour all the shapes with a dot inside to find out!

Answer: Yeti

SPY GAMES!

The gang are practising their secret agent skills!
Can you help complete all the spy tests?

1. LASER MAZE!

The gang need to get to the end of the maze WITHOUT setting off the alarm!
Draw a line from start to finish WITHOUT hitting any lasers!

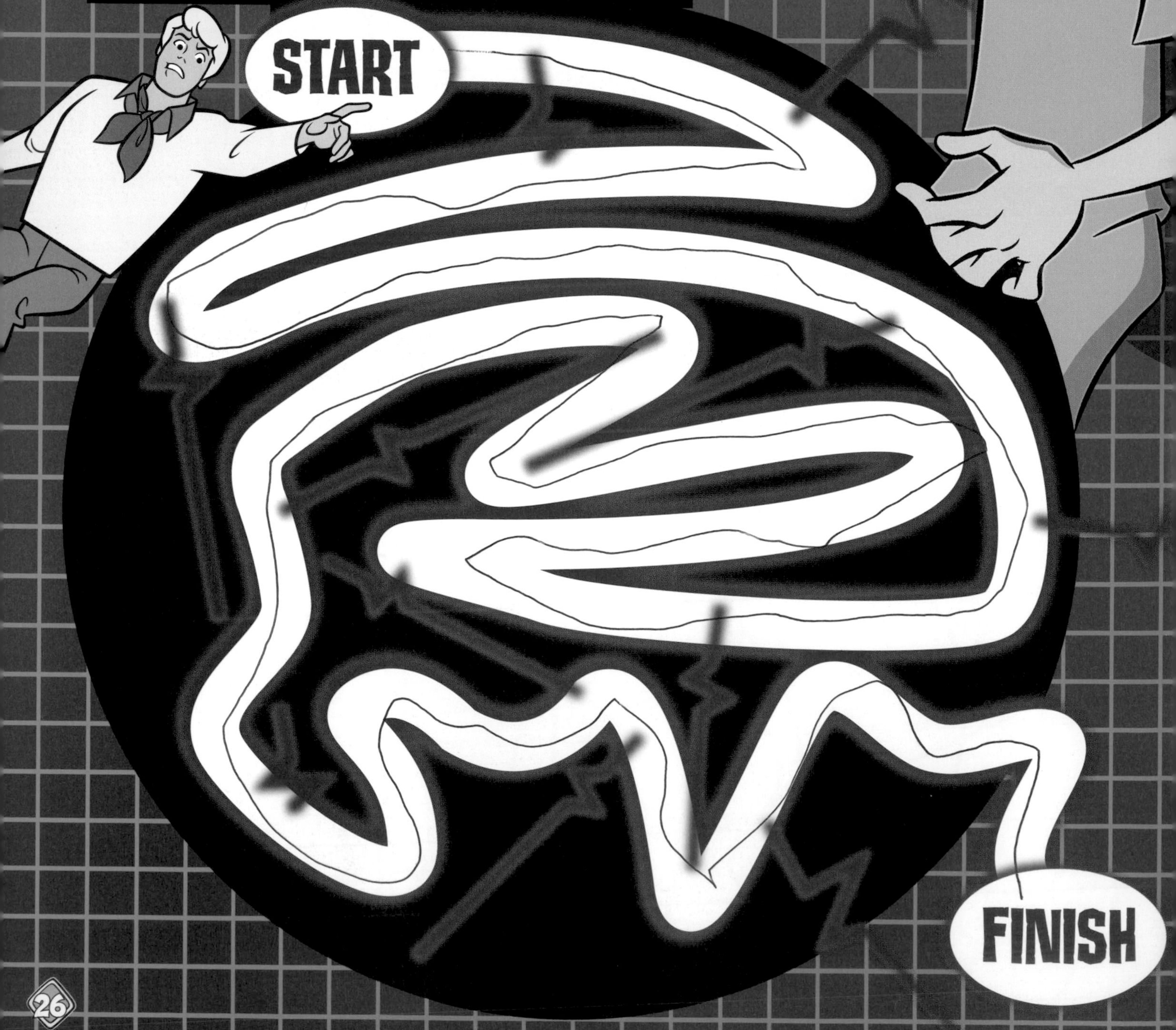

START

FINISH

2. CODE CRACKER!

Well done on the maze! Now for a tougher test! Can you find the hidden word by crossing out every letter that apperas TWICE?

B G D B R O
A P S Q H Z
C N C S Z L
L O R G E Q

Enter left-over letters here to spell the hidden word!

C O R C L E

3. FREAK OR FAKE?

Nice work! Now the final test! Can you tell the difference between a real monster, and a fake? Circle 5 differences!

REAL

FAKE

Answers: 2. Daphne, 3. Pants, tongue, eye patch, hair and tattoo.

CONTINUED FROM PAGE 24

CONTINUED ON PAGE 40

38

SUPER-SLEUTH WORDSEARCH!

Can you find the hidden phrase in this grid? Cross out all the words in the list, then enter the left-over letters in sequence to the grid below!

catch
missing
hidden
theft
find

run
crime
clues

M	C	L	U	E	S	C
I	R	M	Y	F	S	A
S	I	R	T	I	E	T
S	M	U	R	N	Y	C
I	E	N	I	D	N	H
N	C	T	H	E	F	T
G	H	I	D	D	E	N

Enter left-over letters here:

| C | M | Y | T | R | I | N | | Y | E | S |

CONTINUED FROM PAGE 38

Clue Collector!

Can you help the gang find the clues to solve these two crimes?

1)

A rare painting has been stolen from this house. Can you find 3 clues as to who did it?

Dracula did it!

Tick the villain you think it was! ✓

2)

A powerful crystal has been stolen from this tomb! Can you find 3 clues to help find the thief?

Tick the villain you think it was! ✓

Answers: 1) Dracula. 2) Witch.

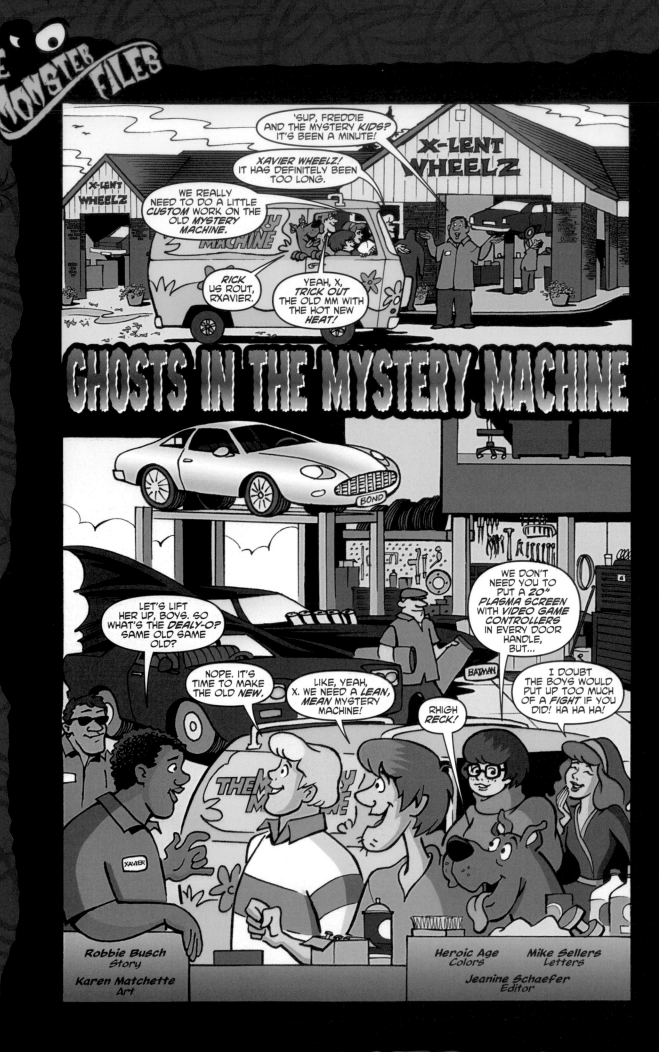

Spooky Skull

This skull saver will keep your pocket money safe!

50

YOU WILL NEED:

a balloon, newspaper, PVA glue, scissors, paints and paintbrush, a pencil, sticky tape, a round plastic tub.

WHAT DID THE SKELETON ORDER AT THE RESTAURANT? A LEMONADE AND A MOP!

Haunted Howlers!

WHAT IS A WEREWOLF'S FAVOURITE DAY OF THE YEAR? HOWL-OWE'EN!

WHAT'S A ZOMBIE'S FAVOURITE CEREAL? RICE KREEPIES!

Cover the balloon with three layers of paper mache but be careful to leave the knotted end uncovered. Stand the balloon in a bowl to make this easier. Leave it to dry and then burst the balloon.

2 Tape the round tub to the base of the balloon. This will make the chin part of the skull.

3 Cut a slot for your money at the top of the skull. Make another small hole on the back of the skull so you can empty your savings out.

4 Cover the whole thing in two layers of paper mache – be careful not to paper over the holes. Paint the whole thing white as this will make a good base colour for decorating it.

ASK AN ADULT TO HELP.

5 Use a pencil to sketch in the eyes, nose and mouth. Now use your paints to decorate the skull with scary colours.

CONTINUED ON PAGE 57

55

Double Trouble!

Can you find the **10** creepy changes we've made to this freaky scene?

Tick each time you spot a change!

Answers: 1. Missing Bat, 2. Velma's glasses, 3. Toadstall's spots, 4. Scooby's missing a spot, 5. Scooby's collar, 6. Mystery Machine, 7. Extra ghost, 8. Spider, 9. Fortune teller, 10. Extra toadstall.

CONTINUED FROM PAGE 55